W9-CXY-459

The Wonderful World of J. Wesley Smith

(An Abridgment)

By BURR SHAFER

SCHOLASTIC BOOK SERVICES

Published by Scholastic Book Services, a division
of Scholastic Magazines, Inc., New York, N.Y.

"It seems that juvenile delinquency is on the increase."

"The defendant hasn't a chance. He's engaged some green lawyer from New Hampshire by the name of Webster."

"I'm in a hurry to get home so I'll go with Ulysses."

"Monticello is a pretty name, Mr. Jefferson, and no doubt it's well constructed—
but the design! I think you ought to sue the architect."

"And another thing. If all us Spartans are warriors, who'll pay the taxes?"

"It's a new unemployment project—Rameses calls it a pyramid."

"I want the design to be conservative. It should look like a
cave or a hollow tree."

"As a preliminary step, I suppose, we might recognize them on a sort of *de facto* basis."

"All I know is that guy named Guy Fawkes asked me to watch these barrels."

"So—on what big deal did you outsmart Baron Rothschild today?"

"But, Cicero, I'm positive Catiline is just a harmless liberal."

"But I can't shoe your horse by tonight, Mr. Revere! I've got Lon Hasset's team to do, and Squire Gordon's bay, and . . ."

"What a relief! It isn't a skull and crossbones, after all, Captain Smith!"

"My trouble is I'm forty thousand years ahead of my time."

"We're so proud of Wesley—he's found a way to take all the
wheat germ out of flour."

"I've heard they're fixed."

"Let's row back to Norway. I couldn't stand another
of these Maine winters."

"I'm too old for any more helter-skelter stuff. I've settled down here as Trotsky's assistant."

"Why don't you rewrite that part about the 'rocket's red glare,' Francis? Rockets are practically obsolete."

"Fellow citizens! Are you tired of having to pay five cents for meat? Ten cents for butter? Twelve cents a dozen for eggs? Then vote for . . . "

"Now, don't drink too much, Ponce. I don't know very much about the problems of teen-agers."

"How are yours on hills?"

"You heard me! Now, take me to your maharajah!"

"I'm sorry, Mr. Thoreau, but Mr. Walden says you can't fish in his pond."

"Move from Egypt? But I've just begun to accumulate some seniority!"

"Dogs and monkeys will fly through the sky in machines that will strike terror into the hearts of men. Horseless carriages will grow bigger and bigger, then smaller and smaller. Women will paint their nails the color of blood, and the paint sellers will have a scandal that will rock the nation . . ."

"But let's be fair about this—Attila has done a lot of good things, too."

"And if you're not out by twelve o'clock, General Washington, I'll have to charge you for another day!"

"That Lady Godiva can't begin to ride a horse as well as I can."

"Bread and circuses! Bread and circuses! What I want is Social Security."

"Ah, good morning, Mrs. Chippendale."

"It isn't the lack of representation that upsets me—it's the taxation."

"Why don't you do a story about me, Mr. Alger? How I inherited this business from my father and . . ."

"But, Monsieur Rousseau—if I go back to nature, how will I have money for any more of your pamphlets?"

"Be careful on these land grants. I've heard he's trying to
stick you with New Jersey."

"Me tell that nosey paleface that Niagara River give him nice safe canoe ride from Lake Erie to Lake Ontario."

"You're right — I picked out the wrong hunting ground, I'm too inexperienced to lead, we need a new chief — I resign."

"Now that poor Count Cadillac has gone back to France, his name will soon be forgotten in this Detroit wilderness."

"Maybe this'll teach you to watch how you change traffic
lanes on the Appian Way."

"Most all-prevailing monarch, ruler of the universe, controller of all things,
master of all fates and destinies, joy of . . . "

"Why don't you physicians write prescriptions in Latin so everyone can understand them?"

"This business of taking from the rich and giving to the poor could easily become a political theory."

"Never mind the emperor—salute the press box."

"It's not that we're afraid, mind you—we just can't afford to
defeat any more countries."

"A funny thing happened to me on the way over to the castle."

"This new generation just hops around with no end in view. When I was young we had war dances and rain dances and they made some sense."

"I don't feel very insulted this morning, do you?"

"I'm leaving this place. Every time I try to drill for water, some black stuff flows up."

"Instead of just sitting there reading Malthus, why don't
you help out around here?"

" '*Morituri te salutamus*'—whatever THAT means."

"Another thing, General Washington, if you were the first President, you wouldn't be able to say you inherited your problems from somebody else."

"Anyone for discus throwing?"

"V—IV—III—II—I—oh, for the love of Mars!"

"Surprise! I've traded in all this old furniture
by Chippendale for modern Victorian."

"No! No! I meant throw the OTHER rascals out!"

"It's called money. The government either gives it to you or takes it away."

"98 . . . 99 . . . 100."

"Frankly, Mr. Stuart, you're in a rut."

"I don't like to box with the Marquis of Queensbury—he keeps
making up his own rules."

"The old girl's daft! She told me that some day John D's grandson would increase my taxes!"

"But this is all wrong — I'M the sheriff and YOU'RE the cattle rustlers!"

"I was Chaucer's secretary—but I got fired because I couldn't spell."

"Something's wrong with our laddie. He's still awake and I've been playing a lullaby for a solid hour."

"But would they remember ten? Maybe you should give them two or three at a time."

"Half a league, half a league, half a league—Mr. Tennyson, can't you come to the point?"

"Stop making promises—you're already elected."

"That will be five years—with ten days added because of the change-over
to the Gregorian calendar."

"All well and good, Mr. Edison—but in a typical small town who's going to volunteer to stay up all night generating electricity?"

"It is unthinkable that the citizens of Rhode Island should ever surrender their sovereignty to some central authority located way off in Philadelphia."

"A vacation? You mean you actually want me to pay you for three days when you won't even be here?"

"I won't collect any more rent from Franz Mesmer, I won't collect any more rent from Franz Mesmer . . ."

"I simply cannot accustom myself to the tempo of modern travel. To think that I left London only two months ago and here I am in New York."

"It's a new-fangled thing the boss bought. I'm quitting Saturday."

"I doubt if a runt like you, Bonaparte, has any qualifications for leadership—
but I'm giving you a try as acting corporal."

"I never could lick these Roman numerals. How much is XXVI plus CLXXIV?"

"I'm afraid we'll have to go back to bronze. This new stuff rusts."

"Happy birthday, sweetheart—I bought you a mummy case."

"It'll never work. People will go blind looking for the right key."

"Try to remember. Was it an oak tree you put the charter in?"

"I've finally perfected my invention. All you have to do is pull it."

"Haven't you any others? This sheet is printed crooked and the word 'Postage' is misspelled."

"No, no, Samson. Apply equal pressure, like this."

"This new calendar—how will it affect charge accounts?"

"Do you mind if I go to lunch early, Professor Pavlov?
For some reason I'm hungry."

"We'll never get anywhere by creating law. If people are going to eat each other, they'll eat each other, that's all."

"Of course, we're only sending up monkeys now, but it won't be long until you see Wesley up there."

"I know I predicted fair and warmer, but let me explain about the sudden appearance of this low-pressure area . . ."

"I'm sorry, Noah, but I have my depositors to think of and a loan on
an ark just doesn't seem . . ."

"Oh, your price for the land is most generous. But, frankly, we were looking for a somewhat better class of customer."

"And so you want to be admired as a brave hunter, but at the same time you're afraid of tigers. That's why your stomach hurts."

"Never mind why—we're moving to Florence and changing the name of the firm."

"Don't bother to outline a program. Just criticize the previous administration."

"Oh, Washington himself is all right. It's the men around him like Jefferson and Adams and . . ."

"I don't like it. It's against nature."

"I'm sorry, Mr. Poe, but you know very well you can't keep a pet in your room."

"Suppose we go into orbit . . ."

"If you ever tasted one of Ellen's wheat-germ loaves, King Alfred, you wouldn't feel so bad about burning it."

"Go ahead and nominate anybody you want—I can't stand tobacco smoke."

"Herr Beethoven says that he is too deaf to hear your new composition, and to thank you for reminding him that his affliction is not always a handicap."

"I see the Dodgers defeating the Yankees in the World Series
—whatever that means."

"And remember on that last Crusade how those oriental
spices upset your stomach."

"I may not be able to hit anything—but this is ONE shot that's going to make a lot of noise."

"I think people will understand you better, Mr. President,
if you just say 'eighty-seven years.'"

"But, Galileo—why should you study moon craters when right here at home most people don't have satisfactory bathrooms yet?"

"Find out who's behind this vicious sabotage. Someone in the paint department has deliberately put two different colors on this motor car."

"Lucky for you, Sir Walter, that I was on hand when that thing caught fire."

"Your cooking is always the same. At the Borgias', things
have fascinating new tastes."

"I think, Mr. Fahrenheit, that most people know when it's hot or cold enough
to take off their coats or light a fire."

"But I'm NOT Dr. Livingston—go away!"

"You'll have to get rid of this junk, Professor Volta. I just touched something and got a terrible shock."

"It's intolerable, General Washington. The farmers of Valley Forge deserve more consideration. Drilling at all hours, drums scaring the livestock, and several chickens stolen. We have friends in the Continental Congress, you know . . ."

"Now, my idea, Your Majesty, is a stamp tax for the American colonies—
it will be painless and easy to collect."

"So much for tigers. Now, suppose we try domesticating reindeer."

"Of course the world is flat—but he's so cute."

"Well, we've lived through this terrible first winter. Now, to clear some ground, take our seed corn, and . . ."

"Let me tell you about the dream I had last night, Dr. Freud!"

"You mean you'd make me PAY to sleep here? Why, a fellow named Procrustes just offered to put me up free!"

"I just wanted to make a musical out of *Pygmalion!*"

"Good heavens—building right on top of us! What's to become
of Coney Island at this rate?"

"—and this is final, Herr Bach. Either you stop this silly composing and spend more time rehearsing the choirboys, or we get a new organist."

"It's a new story by that Dickens fellow—about a worthy banker named Scrooge who finally degenerates into a sentimental weakling."

"Stop calling me Willie Shakesberg, and don't ask me 'What's in a name?'"

"And another thing, Mr. Clemens, I want you to stop these feeble attempts at humor you have been sneaking into your copy."

"Certainly we can find a better governess than that mousy little Miss Brontë."

"No, I didn't commit any crime—they just gave me an aptitude test."

"I've got a better idea—we'll rob from the rich and keep it ourselves."